AYYAPPAN

KING RAJASHEKHARA, THE WEALTHY RULER OF PANTHALAM, IN KERALA, HAD NO CHILDREN.

HIS SUBJECTS WERE WORRIED.

IF THERE IS NO HEIR TO THE THRONE, WHAT WILL BECOME OF US WHEN OUR KING DIES?

O THAT HE WERE BLESSED WITH A SON.

YES. A SON AS PIOUS AND GENEROUS AS HE IS!

HIS AMBITIOUS DIWAN, HOWEVER, WAS HAPPY.

AS LONG AS THERE IS NO HEIR TO THE THRONE, WHEN RAJASHEKHARA DIES HIS KINGDOM WILL CERTAINLY BE MINE.

ONE DAY AS RAJASHEKHARA AND HIS QUEEN SAT TALKING—

ALAS! WHO WILL RULE THE KINGDOM AFTER ME?

LET US PRAY TO LORD SHIVA FOR A SON. I AM SURE HE WILL BLESS US WITH ONE.

YOU ARE RIGHT, MY QUEEN. LET US BEGIN PRAYING TODAY.

FROM THAT DAY RAJASHEKHARA AND HIS WIFE PRAYED FERVENTLY TO LORD SHIVA FOR A SON.

MEANWHILE, FAR AWAY, THE EVIL MAHISHASURA PERFORMED SEVERE PENANCES TO OBTAIN A BOON FROM LORD BRAHMA.

EMBOLDENED BY THE BOON, MAHISHASURA BEGAN HARASSING ALL ON EARTH.

THE EVIL ONE IS HERE!

RUN!

O DEVAS, SAVE US!

THE DEVAS HELD COUNCIL.

THIS ASURA MUST BE DESTROYED. BECAUSE OF BRAHMA'S BOON, ONLY A WOMAN WOULD BE ABLE TO DO IT.

THEN LET US EVOKE ONE WITH OUR COMBINED POWERS.

AS SOON AS THE WOMAN APPEARED BEFORE THEM—

HA! HA! HA!

WE WILL CALL HER CHANDIKA DEVI.

DEVI! GO TO EARTH AND DESTROY THE EVIL MAHISHASURA.

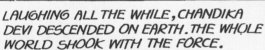

LAUGHING ALL THE WHILE, CHANDIKA DEVI DESCENDED ON EARTH. THE WHOLE WORLD SHOOK WITH THE FORCE.

HA! HA! HA!

WHO IS THAT SENSELESS WOMAN? GO BRING HER TO ME.

BUT CHANDIKA DEVI VANQUISHED THEM IN NO TIME.

THEY RETURNED TO MAHISHASURA.

LORD! WE HAD TO RETREAT.

TAKE THE WHOLE ARMY IF NECESSARY; BUT *BRING HER HERE!*

HOWEVER, THE ARMY WAS NO MATCH EITHER FOR CHANDIKA DEVI. IT WAS SOON ROUTED.

MAHISHASURA WAS MAD WITH ANGER. HE APPROACHED CHANDIKA DEVI FIERCELY...

THAT WOMAN HAS GONE TOO FAR. I SHALL DESTROY HER.

...AND ATTACKED HER.

HA! HA! HA!

BUT HE, TOO, WAS NO MATCH FOR HER AND WAS SOON SLAIN.

HER MISSION ACCOMPLISHED, CHANDIKA DEVI ASCENDED TO HEAVEN.

WHEN MAHISHI, THE WIFE OF MAHISHASURA, LEARNT OF HER HUSBAND'S DEATH—

I SHALL TEACH THE DEVAS A LESSON. IT WAS THEY WHO INVOKED THE DEVI.

MAHISHI UNDERTOOK A DEEP PENANCE TO PROPITIATE LORD BRAHMA. HE APPEARED BEFORE HER.

MAHISHI! WHAT DO YOU DESIRE?

THAT I SHOULD NOT MEET MY DEATH AT THE HANDS OF EITHER VISHNU OR SHIVA!

BRAHMA GRANTED HER THE BOON AND VANISHED.

MAHISHI BEGAN TAUNTING THE DEVAS.

TO WHOM WILL YOU TURN NOW? SHIVA AND VISHNU ARE POWERLESS AGAINST ME.

SHIVA WATCHED AND HEARD ALL.

I MUST PUT AN END TO MAHISHI'S ARROGANCE.

HE WENT TO VISHNU WHO WAS IN THE FORM OF MOHINI, THE ENCHANTRESS.

WE MUST CREATE A SON WHO WILL DESTROY MAHISHI.

WHO WILL REAR THE BABY?

MY DEVOTEES – RAJASHEKHARA AND HIS QUEEN. THEY LONG FOR A CHILD.

I WILL TAKE HIM THERE!

AS SOON AS THE INFANT WAS CREATED—

I WILL TIE THIS GOLD BELL AROUND HIS NECK BEFORE I TAKE HIM TO EARTH.

MEANWHILE, ON EARTH, RAJASHEKHARA WAS OUT HUNTING WITH HIS RETINUE.

AFTER A TIRING DAY WHILE THE PARTY RELAXED ON THE BANKS OF THE RIVER PAMPA...

...RAJASHEKHARA WANDERED OFF ALONE.

HOW PEACEFUL AND QUIET IT IS HERE.

SUDDENLY HE HEARD A FEEBLE WAIL.

WAH! WAH! WAH!

A BABY'S CRY? HERE?

RAJASHEKHARA WALKED IN THE DIRECTION FROM WHICH THE SOUND CAME.

HE SAW A HELPLESS BABY LYING ALL ALONE ON A ROCK.

POOR BABY! DON'T CRY!

HE LOOKED AROUND.

NOT A SOUL IN SIGHT. TO WHOM COULD IT BELONG?

WHAT SHOULD I DO? SHOULD I TAKE HIM HOME? OR SHOULD I LEAVE HIM HERE?

WHILE HE DEBATED WITH HIMSELF A BRAHMAN SUDDENLY APPEARED BEFORE HIM.

DO NOT HESITATE, O KING. TAKE HIM HOME.

BUT WHO IS HE?

YOU WILL KNOW WHEN HE IS TWELVE YEARS OLD.

THEN WHEN THE BRAHMAN WAS ABOUT TO LEAVE—

WAIT! WHAT SHALL I CALL HIM?

CALL HIM MANIKANTHAN, AFTER THE GOLD BELL WHICH HANGS ROUND HIS NECK.

RAJASHEKHARA TOOK MANIKANTHAN HOME TO HIS QUEEN.

A CHILD AT LAST! HOW HAPPY I AM.

HE IS GOD'S OWN GIFT.

BUT RAJASHEKHARA'S DIWAN DIDN'T THINK SO.

THE ACCURSED CHILD! IT HAS UPSET ALL MY PLANS.

MANIKANTHAN SOON GREW UP INTO A STRONG YOUNG LAD.

HE WAS PLACED UNDER THE GUIDANCE OF AN EXCELLENT GURU AND SOON MASTERED ALL THERE WAS TO LEARN.

MANIKANTHAN IS NOT AN ORDINARY CHILD.

BY THE TIME MANIKANTHAN'S STUDIES WERE OVER, THE GURU KNEW THAT HE WAS A DIVINE CHILD.

SIR, PLEASE ACCEPT MY GURU-DAKSHINA.*

FROM YOU I WANT COMPASSION. NOT THESE.

THEN THE GURU BROUGHT HIS BLIND AND MUTE SON BEFORE MANIKANTHAN.

MANIKANTHAN, PLEASE RESTORE HIS SIGHT AND SPEECH.

MANIKANTHAN BLESSED THE BOY.

THEY ARE HIS.

THE GURU'S SON SAW LIGHT.

FATHER! I HAVE BEEN GIVEN A NEW LIFE!

AFTER THIS FIRST MIRACLE MANIKANTHAN PERFORMED MANY MORE. THE NEWS SPREAD.

I HAVE NEVER SEEN SUCH A GIFTED BOY.

OUR FUTURE IS ASSURED. HE WILL SUCCEED THE KING.

THE DIWAN, WHO OVERHEARD THESE COMMENTS...

*THE TRADITIONAL TRIBUTE GIVEN BY A DISCIPLE TO HIS TEACHER

...GOT REALLY WORRIED.

I MUST GET RID OF THE BOY SOMEHOW.

AND THEN THE UNFORESEEN HAPPENED. THE QUEEN GAVE BIRTH TO A SON.

ALAS! WHY WERE YOU NOT BORN EARLIER? NOW YOU WILL NEVER BECOME KING. UNLESS...

THE DIWAN WAS JUBILANT.

THE THRONE SHALL YET BE MINE!

A FEW DAYS LATER HE WENT TO THE QUEEN.

MANIKANTHAN WILL SOON BE TWELVE YEARS OLD. HE WILL THEN BE CROWNED HEIR APPARENT.

WITH THAT, YOUR OWN SON WILL LOSE ALL CHANCES OF EVER BECOMING THE RULER.

WHAT CAN I DO? I AM HELPLESS.

WILL YOU DO AS I TELL YOU? FOR THE SAKE OF YOUR OWN SON?

I WILL. FOR MY SON I WILL DO ANYTHING.

THEN PRETEND TO HAVE A SEVERE HEADACHE. LEAVE THE REST TO ME.

THE DIWAN THEN WENT TO THE COURT PHYSICIAN.

DO AS I TELL YOU AND YOU WILL BE WELL REWARDED.

SPEAK!

16

THE QUEEN HAS A SEVERE HEADACHE. YOU WILL PRESCRIBE TIGRESS'S MILK AS THE ONLY REMEDY.

VERY WELL.

JUST THEN A MESSENGER CAME TO THE PHYSICIAN.

THE QUEEN IS IN AGONY. THE KING HAS ASKED YOU TO EXAMINE HER IMMEDIATELY.

AFTER THE PHYSICIAN HAD EXAMINED THE QUEEN—

WHAT IS THE QUICKEST REMEDY? I CANNOT BEAR TO SEE MY QUEEN IN PAIN.

THE ONLY REMEDY FOR THIS AILMENT IS TIGRESS'S MILK.

THE KING WAS AGHAST.

TIGRESS'S MILK? BUT HOW ARE WE TO GET IT?

THE KING THOUGHT ABOUT IT FOR A WHILE AND THEN SENT FOR HIS DIWAN.

SEND AS MANY MEN AS POSSIBLE INTO THE FOREST IN SEARCH OF TIGRESS'S MILK. THE ONE WHO BRINGS IT SHALL HAVE HALF MY KINGDOM.

MANY MEN WENT BUT ALL RETURNED— UNSUCCESSFUL.

WE SAW A NUMBER OF TIGERS. BUT...

THEN, EXACTLY AS THE WICKED DIWAN HAD FORESEEN —

FATHER, LET ME GO ON THIS ERRAND!

MANIKANTHAN, NO! YOU ARE TOO YOUNG.

FOR MY MOTHER'S SAKE LET ME GO, FATHER.

HOW CAN I LET YOU GO ON SUCH A DANGEROUS VENTURE.

BUT MANIKANTHAN PERSISTED AND RAJASHEKHARA HAD TO YIELD.

ALL RIGHT, MY SON. GO IF YOU MUST. BUT TAKE CARE.

MANIKANTHAN SET OUT FOR THE FOREST.

AS HE WANDERED DEEPER AND DEEPER INTO IT HE CAME TO THE DOMAIN OF MAHISHI, WHO LIVED IN THAT FOREST.

WHO IS THIS CREATURE WHO DARES TO TRESPASS ON OUR FOREST? I MUST TELL MY MISTRESS.

THE ASURA RAN TO MAHISHI.

THERE IS A BOY ROAMING IN OUR FORESTS.

HOW DARE HE, WITHOUT MY PERMISSION! I'LL DESTROY HIM.

MAHISHI WENT UP TO MANIKANTHAN AND ATTACKED HIM.

COME, MAHISHI. MY EARTHLY MISSION IS ABOUT TO BE FULFILLED.

A FIERCE BATTLE ENSUED.

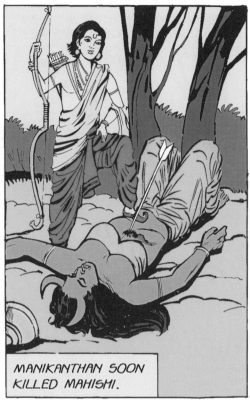

MANIKANTHAN SOON KILLED MAHISHI.

AS MANIKANTHAN CONTINUED HIS SEARCH FOR A TIGRESS, INDRA, KING OF THE DEVAS, APPEARED BEFORE HIM.

I SHALL TAKE THE FORM OF A TIGRESS AND COME WITH YOU INTO THE CITY AS YOUR MOUNT.

THE DEVAS WHO HAD ACCOMPANIED INDRA ALSO TURNED THEMSELVES INTO TIGRESSES.

WE WILL FOLLOW YOU INTO THE CITY.

AS MANIKANTHAN RODE INTO THE CITY ON HIS TERRIFYING MOUNT FOLLOWED BY AN EQUALLY TERRIFYING RETINUE—

TIGERS!

HELP!

RUN!

ONE OF THE CITIZENS RAN TO RAJASHEKHARA.

MANIKANTHAN HAS RETURNED... WITH A HORDE OF TIGRESSES.

THE KING, WHO RUSHED OUT TO SEE THIS UNUSUAL SIGHT, WAS STUNNED.

MANIKANTHAN IS TWELVE TODAY. TODAY I WILL KNOW WHO HE IS.

JUST THEN HE HEARD A DIVINE VOICE.

MANIKANTHAN IS NONE BUT GOD HIMSELF.

RAJASHEKHARA RAN FORWARD AND FELL AT MANIKANTHAN'S FEET.

PLEASE SEND THE TIGRESSES AWAY, MANIKANTHAN. MY PEOPLE ARE TERROR-STRICKEN.

MANIKANTHAN SMILED, AND THE TIGRESSES VANISHED.

AS SOON AS YOU LEFT, THE QUEEN RECOVERED. I BECAME SUSPICIOUS.

MY SUSPICIONS WERE CONFIRMED WHEN I OVERHEARD A CONVERSATION BETWEEN HER AND MY DIWAN.

I SHALL PUNISH THEM FOR THIS.

SPARE THEM. THEY HASTENED MY MISSION OF SLAYING MAHISHI.

AND NOW I MUST LEAVE THIS WORLD.

LORD, A LAST REQUEST. SHOW ME THE PLACE IN MY KINGDOM WHERE I MAY BUILD A TEMPLE FOR YOU.

I AM PLEASED. BUILD IT WHERE THIS ARROW I SHOOT FALLS.

YOU MAY OBSERVE THE PATH OF THE ARROW.

THE ARROW FELL AT THE SUMMIT OF THE SHABARI HILLS.

LET THERE BE JUST EIGHTEEN STEPS LEADING TO THE TEMPLE AT THE EASTERN GATE.

MANIKANTHAN VANISHED AND THE KING BEGAN HIS TREK TO THE MOUNTAIN TOP.

IT IS SO HIGH... IMPOSSIBLE.

AT LAST RAJASHEKHARA REACHED THE TOP OF THE MOUNTAIN.

HOW WILL I EVER ACHIEVE MY TASK?

AS HE STOOD THERE, DAZED WONDERING WHERE TO BEGIN—

I SHALL SEND VISHWAKARMA TO HELP YOU OUT.

UNDER THE GUIDANCE OF VISHWAKARMA, THE DIVINE ARCHITECT...

...THE MAGNIFICENT TEMPLE WAS SOON COMPLETED.

THROUGH THE LORD'S GRACE IT HAS RISEN — NOBLE AND IMPOSING.

WILL I FIND A BEFITTING IDOL NOW?

LORD VISHNU DIVINED THE KING'S ANXIETY. HE SENT FOR PARASHURAMA.

GO DOWN TO EARTH AS A STONE-CARVER AND HELP RAJASHEKHARA INSTALL THE IDOL.

PARASHURAMA LEFT FOR RAJASHEKHARA'S PALACE IN THE GARB OF A SCULPTOR.

AT THE KING'S COURT—

I HAVE HEARD OF YOUR PROBLEM. I MAY BE ABLE TO HELP.

SHOW ME YOUR WARES BEFORE YOU TAKE UP THE CHALLENGING TASK.

THEY ARE FLAW-LESS, EACH ONE OF THEM.

YOU ARE NO ORDINARY SCULPTOR. TELL ME THE TRUTH. WHO ARE YOU?

I AM PARASHURAMA. I HAVE ALREADY FASHIONED THE IDOL.

PARASHURAMA ASSUMED HIS OWN FORM.

TODAY, THE DAY OF MAKARA SANKRANTI, IS AUSPICIOUS. I SHALL INSTALL THE IDOL STRAIGHTAWAY.

...AND THUS IT WAS THAT THE IMAGE OF AYYAPPA, AS MANIKANTHAN CAME TO BE POPULARLY KNOWN, WAS SANCTIFIED.

MEANWHILE THE WICKED DIWAN WAS AFFLICTED BY AN INCURABLE DISEASE.

I HAVE SINNED. WILL I EVER BE CLEANSED?

ONE NIGHT HE HAD A DREAM.

COME TO MY TEMPLE ON THE SHABARI HILL. BUT ENTER ONLY AFTER CLEANSING YOURSELF IN THE PAMPA.*

THE DIWAN WASTED NO TIME. THE NEXT MORNING HE SET OUT FOR THE PAMPA.

I HAVE COME TO WASH AWAY MY SINS IN REMORSE, HOLY MOTHER. SAVE ME.

THE DIWAN CAME OUT OF THE WATER GLOWING WITH HEALTH—

I AM CLEANSED. THE HOLY MOTHER HAS BEEN MERCIFUL.

* RIVER SAID TO BE ENLIVENED BY THE SPIRIT OF SHABARI. THE DEVOTEE OF

THEN WITHOUT PAUSING FOR BREATH HE RAN UP TO THE TEMPLE.

AYYAPPA! AYYAPPA!

WHEN HE REACHED THE SANCTUM SANCTORUM, OVERCOME BY EMOTION HE FELL AT THE FEET OF THE IDOL.

SWAMIYE SHARANAM AYYAPPA!

AND TO THIS DAY AS PILGRIMS MAKE THEIR WAY TO THE TEMPLE OF AYYAPPA, THEY CALL OUT 'SWAMIYE SHARANAM AYYAPPA'.

Amar Chitra Katha's

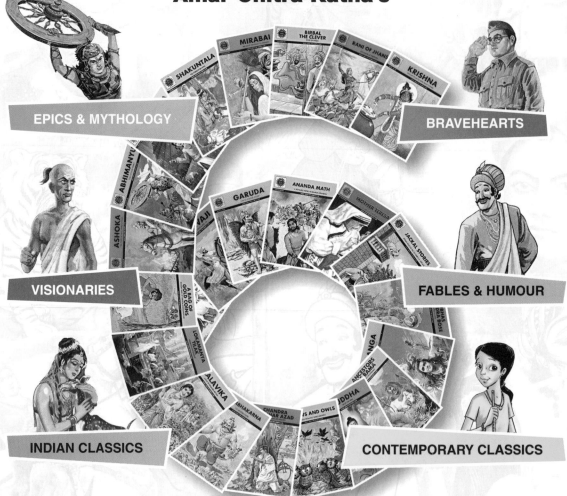

EPICS & MYTHOLOGY

BRAVEHEARTS

VISIONARIES

FABLES & HUMOUR

INDIAN CLASSICS

CONTEMPORARY CLASSICS

EXCITING STORY CATEGORIES,
ONE AMAZING DESTINATION.

From the episodes of Mahabharata to the wit of Birbal,
from the valour of Shivaji to the teachings of Tagore,
from the adventures of Pratapan to the tales of Ruskin Bond –
Amar Chitra Katha stories span across different genres to get you the best of literature.

GANESHA

THE REMOVER OF ALL OBSTACLES

The route to your roots

GANESHA

Ganesha revered in India as the remover of obstacles is first and foremost an obedient son. Standing guard at his mother's door, this son of Parvati refuses to let anyone through. Even Lord Shiva is denied entry! This confrontation between father and son has one beneficial outcome – the emergence of Ganesha, the elephant- headed god of wisdom.

Script
Kamala Chandrakant

Illustrations
C.M. Vitankar

Editor
Anant Pai

GANESHA

ONE DAY, PARVATI, SHIVA'S WIFE, POSTED NANDI, HIS GANA,* AT THE DOOR TO HER PALACE.

I AM GOING TO HAVE MY BATH. DO NOT LET ANYONE ENTER AND DISTURB ME.

A LITTLE LATER, SHIVA CAME THERE. NANDI WAS IN A DILEMMA.

WHAT SHOULD I DO? HOW CAN I STOP HIM FROM ENTERING HIS OWN HOME?

* ATTENDANT.

1

SHIVA ENTERED THE PALACE AND STRODE INTO THE INNER ROOMS.

MY LORD, HERE? BUT NANDI WAS TOLD...

NANDI HAS DISOBEYED ME. YOU MAY BE MY HUSBAND BUT HE HAD NO RIGHT TO LET YOU ENTER!

HA! HA!

SHIVA WAS AMUSED BUT PARVATI WAS ANNOYED.

I MUST HAVE A GANA OF MY OWN WHO WILL OBEY ME ALONE.

SHE SPOKE TO HER FRIENDS ABOUT IT.

YOU ARE RIGHT. NONE OF THE GANAS CAN REALLY BE CALLED YOUR OWN.

ONE OF THEM HAD AN IDEA.

WHY DON'T YOU CREATE A GANA WHO WILL OWE FIRST ALLEGIANCE TO YOU?

A GOOD SUGGESTION. I SHALL.

SHE GATHERED THE SAFFRON PASTE FROM HER OWN BODY AND CREATED A BOY.

WHEN SHE FINISHED, SHE GAZED IN ADMIRATION AT HER OWN CREATION.

HOW HANDSOME HE IS! HOW STRONG HE LOOKS!

SHE DECKED HIM WITH ORNAMENTS AND BLESSED HIM. THEN —

YOU ARE MY SON — MY VERY OWN SON. I HAVE NONE ELSE TO CALL MY OWN.

COMMAND ME, MOTHER. WHAT SHOULD I DO?

TAKE THIS STAFF AND FOLLOW ME.

SHE LED HIM TO THE DOOR.

STAND HERE AND LET NO ONE ENTER WITHOUT MY PERMISSION.

A LITTLE LATER —

WHO COULD THAT BOY BE? I HAVE NEVER SEEN HIM BEFORE.

TO SHIVA'S ASTONISHMENT, THE YOUTH BARRED HIS WAY.

HALT! NO ONE ENTERS WITHOUT MY MOTHER'S PERMISSION.

SHIVA WAS TAKEN ABACK.

FOOLISH BOY! DO YOU KNOW WHO I AM? MOVE OUT OF MY WAY.

WITHOUT UTTERING A WORD, THE YOUTH STRUCK SHIVA WITH HIS STAFF.

SHIVA WAS FURIOUS.

FOOL! I AM SHIVA, PARVATI'S HUSBAND. HOW DARE YOU FORBID ME TO ENTER MY OWN HOME!

BUT THE YOUTH ONLY RAISED HIS STAFF AND HIT SHIVA ONCE AGAIN.

SHIVA TURNED TO HIS GANAS.

WHO IS THAT FOOL? WHAT IS HE DOING THERE? THROW HIM OUT AND REPORT TO ME.

SHIVA LEFT AND THE GANAS TURNED UPON THE YOUTH.

GET AWAY WITH YOU OR YOU WILL RECEIVE A TASTE OF MY VALOUR.

YOU GET AWAY FROM HERE, IF YOU VALUE YOUR LIFE.

YOU SEEM TO FORGET THAT WE ARE SHIVA'S GANAS.

THE YOUTH STOOD STILL FOR A WHILE. HE WAS PUZZLED.

SHIVA IS MY MOTHER'S LORD. WHAT SHOULD I DO? SHOULD I FIGHT THEM OR SHOULDN'T I?

MEANWHILE, INDOORS PARVATI HAD HEARD THE COMMOTION. SHE SENT HER FRIEND OUT.

PLEASE FIND OUT WHAT THAT NOISE IS ALL ABOUT.

THE FRIEND SOON RETURNED.

THEY ARE THREATENING YOUR SON. PLEASE DON'T ALLOW THEM TO LOWER YOUR PRESTIGE.

PARVATI HESITATED FOR A MOMENT.

SHIVA IS AFTER ALL MY HUSBAND...

BUT WHY DID HE TRY TO FORCE HIS WAY IN? LET WHAT HAS TO HAPPEN, HAPPEN.

SHE SENT THE FRIEND OUT ONCE AGAIN.

TELL MY SON NOT TO GIVE IN TO **ANYONE.**

THE FRIEND CAME OUT.

GENTLE SIR, YOUR MOTHER SAYS THAT YOU SHOULD NOT LET ANYONE ENTER.

THE BOY WAS NO LONGER IN DOUBT. HE TURNED TO THE GANAS.

I AM THE SON OF PARVATI. YOU ARE THE GANAS OF SHIVA. YOU MUST CARRY OUT HIS ORDERS AND I — HERS.

I REPEAT, SHIVA SHALL NOT ENTER WITHOUT MY MOTHER'S PERMISSION.

NOW, THE GANAS WERE DOUBTFUL.

HE IS PARVATI'S SON. WHAT SHOULD WE DO? WOULD SHIVA STILL WANT US TO THROW HIM OUT?

THEY REPORTED TO SHIVA.

LORD, IT IS PARVATI'S **OWN** SON WHO REFUSES TO LET YOU IN.

ALAS, PARVATI! YOU HAVE GONE TOO FAR. YOU HAVE LEFT ME WITH NO ALTERNATIVE.

IF I TELL MY GANAS TO WITHDRAW, IT WILL BE SAID THAT I WAS SUBSERVIENT TO MY WIFE. MY GANAS WILL HAVE TO FIGHT HIM.

HE TURNED TO HIS GANAS.

ALL OF YOU ARE MY OWN, INCLUDING PARVATI'S SON. SO A BATTLE MAY NOT SEEM PROPER TO YOU.

BUT IF WE DON'T ACCEPT THE CHALLENGE, WE MAY BE MISUNDERSTOOD. GO! FIGHT AND DEFEAT HIM. IT SHOULD BE EASY.

SO THE GANAS, FULLY ARRAYED FOR WAR, WENT BACK TO THE BOY. HE WAS AMUSED WHEN HE SAW THEM.

I, A MERE BOY CARRYING OUT MY MOTHER'S ORDERS, WEL- COME YOU, THE LEADERS OF SHIVA'S HORDES.

THE GANAS RUSHED AT HIM.

NANDI GRABBED HIS LEGS.

BUT—

HA! THAT'S BETTER.

AA..A.AH!

MANY OF THE GANAS FELL.

THE REST FLED AS FAST AS THEY COULD.

THE BOY ONCE AGAIN TOOK HIS POST AT THE DOOR.

MEANWHILE, WHEN BRAHMA, VISHNU AND INDRA HEARD THE UPROAR, THEY TALKED THE MATTER OVER WITH SAGE NARADA.

GO TO LORD SHIVA. HE MAY NEED YOU.

THEY WENT ACCORDINGLY AND BOWED BEFORE SHIVA.

LORD, WE ARE HERE TO DO YOUR BIDDING.

SHIVA TOLD THEM ALL.

...AND HE DARES TO PREVENT ME FROM ENTERING MY OWN HOME.

O BRAHMA, GO THERE AND TRY TO BRING HIM UNDER CONTROL.

I SHALL GO DISGUISED AS A BRAHMAN.

ACCOMPANIED BY MANY SAGES, BRAHMA LEFT ON HIS MISSION.

AS THEY NEARED HIM, THE YOUTH SUDDENLY JUMPED FORWARD AND —

THAT SHOULD TEACH YOU A LESSON.

BRAHMA WAS TAKEN UNAWARES.

I HAVE NOT COME TO FIGHT. I HAVE COME TO MAKE PEACE. LISTEN TO ME!

FOR AN ANSWER, THE YOUTH LIFTED HIS CLUB MENACINGLY.

HA! RUN. I SHALL NEVER FAIL MY MOTHER.

MEANWHILE, THE SAGES RAN TO SHIVA.

THIS MATTER HAS GONE TOO FAR. THE BOY MUST BE DESTROYED.

HE SENT FOR HIS SON, KARTIKEYA, AND INDRA, THE KING OF THE DEVAS.

LEAD YOUR GANAS AND DEVAS TO WAR. VANQUISH THE IMPUDENT UPSTART.

THE DEVAS, LED BY INDRA, AND THE GANAS, BY KARTIKEYA, FELL UPON THE BOY FROM ALL DIRECTIONS.

BUT THE BOY FACED THEM VALIANTLY.

MEANWHILE, PARVATI LEARNED OF ALL THAT HAD HAPPENED. SHE WAS FURIOUS.

HOW DARE THEY HARASS MY SON!

THEN AND THERE SHE CREATED THE TWO SHAKTIS, KALI AND DURGA.

GO! ASSIST MY SON.

KALI STOOD BETWEEN THE BOY AND THE ENEMY. OPENING HER MOUTH WIDE, SHE SWALLOWED THEIR WEAPONS...

...AND HURLED THEM BACK.

DURGA TOOK THE FORM OF LIGHTNING...

...AND DESTROYED THE ENEMIES' WEAPONS BEFORE THEY COULD REACH THE BOY.

BETWEEN THE TWO OF THEM THEY DID NOT LET A SINGLE WEAPON COME ANYWHERE NEAR THE BOY'S SWINGING CLUB.

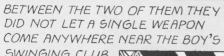

INDRA AND HIS DEVAS WERE COMPLETELY ROUTED.

EVEN KARTIKEYA, WHO HAD KILLED THE INVINCIBLE TARAKASURA, WAS HELPLESS.

THEY HELD COUNCIL.

WHAT SHOULD WE DO?

LET US GO BACK TO SHIVA.

O LORD, WE HAVE SEEN AND HEARD OF MANY BATTLES BUT NEVER HAVE WE SEEN OR HEARD OF SUCH A WARRIOR!

THEIR PRAISE ONLY INFURIATED SHIVA.

I WILL HAVE TO KILL HIM WITH MY OWN HANDS.

SHIVA THUNDERED OUT FOLLOWED BY ALL OF THEM..

UNPERTURBED BY THE SIGHT OF SHIVA, THE BOY ATTACKED ALL THE CHIEF GODS. ONE BY ONE THEY FELL.

AS SHIVA WATCHED HIM FIGHT, HE WAS AMAZED.

HE IS INVINCIBLE. HE CAN ONLY BE KILLED BY CUNNING. I MUST WATCH FOR AN OPPORTUNITY.

THE SAME THOUGHT HAD STRUCK VISHNU TOO. HE SPOKE TO SHIVA.

I SHALL USE MY POWERS OF DELUSION TO FIGHT HIM, IF YOU PERMIT ME.

YOU MAY. THAT IS THE ONLY WAY.

BUT KALI AND DURGA DIVINED THEIR INTENTIONS.

WHAT SHOULD WE DO?

LET US CONFER ALL OUR STRENGTH ON THE YOUTH. ! THEN EVEN VISHNU'S MAYA WILL PROVE INEFFECTUAL.

WITH THE ADDED STRENGTH OF THE TWO SHAKTIS, THE BOY SWUNG HIS CLUB AT VISHNU.

VISHNU HAD TO USE ALL HIS ENERGY TO DODGE IT.

SHIVA SAW HIS PLIGHT AND CHARGED WITH HIS TRIDENT.

BUT—

SHIVA TOOK UP HIS BOW.

THE BOY DASHED IT TO THE GROUND WITH HIS CLUB.

NO WONDER MY GANAS WERE HELPLESS.

THE NEXT MOMENT—

HE'S BACK.

THE BOY LIFTED HIS CLUB...

...BUT IT WAS CUT IN TWO BY VISHNU'S DISCUS.

THE BOY HURLED THE PIECE THAT WAS LEFT IN HIS HAND...

... BUT VISHNU'S MOUNT, GARUDA, CAUGHT IT AND PROTECTED HIS MASTER.

THEN, AS THE BOY PICKED UP HIS STAFF TO HIT VISHNU, SHIVA CAME UP FROM BEHIND AND...

...CUT OFF HIS HEAD.

FOR A MOMENT ALL ON THE SCENE STOOD STILL, THEIR GAZE FIXED ON THE VALIANT HERO.

THEN THE DEVAS AND THE GANAS BECAME JUBILANT.

BUT SHIVA WAS TROUBLED.

ALAS! WHAT HAVE I DONE? HOW SHALL I FACE PARVATI? HE WAS CREATED BY HER. THAT MADE HIM MY SON TOO.

MEANWHILE, WHEN PARVATI LEARNT OF HER SON'S DEATH—

MY SON WAS KILLED BY UNFAIR MEANS. FOR THIS THE DEVAS AND GANAS SHALL ALL DIE.

THEY PROPITIATED PARVATI AND PLEADED FOR MERCY.

O GREAT GODDESS, HAVE MERCY ON US. WE SHALL ACCOMPLISH WHATEVER YOU ASK OF US. FORGIVE US.

I WILL. BUT MY SON MUST REGAIN HIS LIFE AND MUST HAVE AN HONOUR- ABLE STATUS AMONG YOU.

THEY WENT TO SHIVA AND PUT PARVATI'S CONDITIONS BEFORE HIM.

IT SHALL BE DONE. FOR THE SAKE OF PEACE AND HAPPINESS.

GO NORTH. BRING THE HEAD OF THE FIRST CREA- TURE THAT CROSSES YOUR PATH. FIT THAT HEAD TO THE BOY'S BODY AND IT WILL COME TO LIFE.

IT WAS A SINGLE-TUSKED ELEPHANT THAT MET THEM.

THEY BROUGHT THE HEAD BACK AND FITTED IT TO THE BODY OF THE BOY.

THE BOY SAT UP.

DELIGHTED, THEY SHOWED HIM TO PARVATI. BUT SHE WAS ONLY PARTIALLY APPEASED.

WHAT ABOUT HIS STATUS?

AT THAT MOMENT INDRA AND THE OTHER GODS LED SHIVA TO HER.

SHIVA BOWED BEFORE PARVATI.

FORGIVE ME, PARVATI. ARROGANCE IS CHARACTERISTIC OF THE MALE. THIS VALIANT YOUTH SHALL BE ANOTHER SON OF MINE.

THEN SHIVA PLACED HIS HAND ON THE BOY'S HEAD.

EVEN AS A MERE BOY YOU SHOWED GREAT VALOUR. YOU SHALL BE GANESHA, THE PRESIDING OFFICER OF ALL MY GANAS. YOU SHALL BE WORTHY OF WORSHIP FOREVER. YOU SHALL ALSO BE CALLED VIGHNESHWARA, THE QUELLER OF OBSTACLES.

SHIVA AND PARVATI ONCE AGAIN BEGAN TO LIVE HAPPILY IN THEIR ABODE AT MOUNT KAILAS, DELIGHTED BY THE PRESENCE OF THEIR TWO SONS. TO THIS DAY, BEFORE ANY VENTURE IS UNDERTAKEN, IT IS GANESHA WHO IS INVOKED AND WHOSE BLESSINGS ARE SOUGHT.

KARTTIKEYA

A SON OF SHIVA

KARTTIKEYA

The Puranas describe Karttikeya, a son of Shiva, as the commander-in-chief of the celestial army. He is also known as Subrahmanya, Skanda, Guha and Kumara. To the Tamil-speaking people he is Murugan. The six-headed, twelve-armed Karttikeya seated on a peacock is the symbol of youth, beauty, valour and supreme wisdom.

Script
Pradip Bhattacharya
& Meera Ugra

Illustrations
C.M.Vitankar

Editor
Anant Pai

This Amar Chitra Katha is based on the Tamil version of Skanda-Purana-Samhita.

KARTTIKEYA

IN ANCIENT TIMES, THE DEVAS AND THE ASURAS WERE FOREVER AT WAR AND OFTEN IT WAS THE ASURAS WHO WERE DEFEATED.

AFTER ONE CRUSHING DEFEAT, AN ASURA KING NAMED AKHIRSEN WENT TO HIS DAUGHTER, MAYA, A SORCERESS.

THE DEVAS ARE VICTORIOUS AGAIN. O THE SHAME OF IT!

DON'T WORRY, FATHER. I WILL NOT REST TILL I TEACH THE DEVAS A LESSON!

TAKING THE FORM OF A BEAUTIFUL WOMAN MAYA WENT TO THE FOREST WHERE THE GREAT SAGE KASHYAPA SAT DEEP IN MEDITATION.

I WILL MARRY THIS SAGE AND BRING FORTH CHILDREN MORE POWERFUL THAN THE DEVAS.

HER MAGIC CHANGED THE PLACE INTO A PRETTY GARDEN WHERE SHE DANCED AND SANG MELODIOUSLY...

...TILL THE SAGE LOOKED UP.

PLEASE LET ME SERVE YOU AS YOUR WIFE, O HOLY ONE.

HOW CAN I REFUSE YOU, NOBLE MAIDEN!

SAGE KASHYAPA AND THE ASURA PRINCESS LIVED HAPPILY IN THE FOREST. IN DUE COURSE A SON WAS BORN TO THEM.

YOU, MY MIGHTY SURAPADMAN, SHALL BE THE LORD OF THE THREE WORLDS.

LATER MAYA GAVE BIRTH TO TWO MORE SONS WHOM SHE NAMED SIMHAMUKHA AND TARAKA.

I CAN'T WAIT FOR THE DAY WHEN YOU WILL CONQUER THE DEVAS AND MAKE THEM OUR SLAVES.

THE VIRTUOUS SAGE OF COURSE WAS IGNORANT OF MAYA'S DESIGNS.

SO WHEN THE BOYS CAME OF AGE—

I AM GOING AWAY, MY SONS. TAKE CARE OF YOUR MOTHER, LEAD A VIRTUOUS LIFE AND BE DEVOTED TO THE LORD.

NOW IS THE TIME TO ACT. PROPITIATE LORD SHIVA AND OBTAIN BOONS WHICH WILL MAKE YOU INVINCIBLE.

AS YOU WISH, MOTHER.

THE THREE LEFT HOME AND PERFORMED SEVERE PENANCES TO WIN THE GRACE OF SHIVA.

BUT THEIR EFFORTS DID NOT BEAR FRUIT. SO SURAPADMAN, THE ELDEST, JUMPED INTO THE SACRIFICIAL FIRE.

BUT THE NEXT MOMENT HE WAS SAVED FROM ITS FLAMES BY SHIVA HIMSELF.

WHY ARE YOU SACRIFICING YOURSELF?

LORD, I WANT TO BE THE MASTER OF THE UNIVERSE. I WANT TO HAVE A BODY THAT WILL NOT PERISH.

NO ONE CAN HAVE AN IMMORTAL BODY. BUT YOU WILL BE INVINCIBLE AND RULE THE UNIVERSE FOR A LONG TIME TO COME.

YOU SHALL NOT BE DEFEATED BY ANY POWER EXCEPT MINE.

INTOXICATED WITH TRIUMPH, THE THREE BROTHERS RETURNED HOME AND TOLD HEIR MOTHER ABOUT SHIVA'S BOON.

AT LAST MY DREAM WILL COME TRUE.

YES, WE DON'T HAVE TO FEAR ANYONE. WE'LL SOON DRIVE THE DEVAS OUT OF HEAVEN.

THEN, RAVAGING KINGDOM AFTER KINGDOM ON THEIR ROUTE...

...THEY CAME TO DEVALOKA. THERE, IN THE FIERCE BATTLE THAT FOLLOWED, THE DEVAS WERE ROUTED...

...AND TAKEN CAPTIVE.

LATER—

HA! HA! HOW DOES IT FEEL TO BE IN BONDAGE, O INDRA, KING OF THE DEVAS?

IS THAT **VAYU**? HOW DEFLATED HE LOOKS!

WHAT SHOULD WE DO WITH THEM, BROTHER?

WE'LL MAKE THEM OUR SLAVES. INDRA WILL BE OUR FISHERMAN, AND VAYU OUR SWEEPER. AND...

...SURYA WILL MAKE A FINE BALL FOR OUR CHILDREN.

A BRILLIANT IDEA! HAHAHA!

SURAPADMAN HAD A MAGNIFICENT CITY BUILT BY VISHWAKARMA, THE ARCHITECT OF THE DEVAS. HE CALLED IT MAHENDRAPURI AND MADE IT HIS CAPITAL.

THE DEVAS MEANWHILE WERE LAMENTING THEIR FATE.

THEY HAVE IMPRISONED EVEN THE VALIANT JAYANTA*! WHAT SHALL WE DO?

HOW LONG CAN WE SUFFER THIS HUMILIATION?

SHIVA HAD PROMISED TO HELP US.

THAT WAS LONG AGO.

* INDRA'S SON

6

LET'S GO TO KAILAS ONCE MORE AND PRAY TO HIM.

HAVE YOU FORGOTTEN WHAT HAPPENED TO KAMA WHEN WE LAST VISITED KAILAS?

KAMA, THE GOD OF LOVE, HAD BEEN BURNT TO ASHES WHEN HE HAD TRIED TO DISTURB SHIVA'S PENANCE. LATER, HOWEVER, HE WAS RESTORED TO LIFE.

SHIVA, HAPPILY MARRIED TO PARVATI NOW, IS MORE COMPASSIONATE AND WILL SURELY LISTEN TO OUR PRAYER.

YES. LET'S GO TO KAILAS ONCE MORE.

AT KAILAS—

LORD, DRUNK WITH POWER THE MEAN ASURAS HAVE MADE US THEIR SLAVES. MY SON, JAYANTA IS THEIR PRISONER!

BE PATIENT! YOUR MISERIES WILL SOON END BECAUSE THEIR DAYS ARE NUMBERED.

THEN SHIVA ASSUMED A FORM WITH SIX FACES···

···FROM WHICH SIX DIVINE SPARKS SHOT FORTH···

···DAZZLING THE DEVAS WITH THEIR SPLENDOUR.

THE CHILD BORN OUT OF THESE SPARKS WILL SLAY THE ASURAS.

SHIVA THEN ASSUMED HIS ORIGINAL FORM.

VAYU, YOU AND AGNI CARRY THESE SPARKS TO GANGA. SHE'LL CARRY THEM TO THE SHARAVANA* ON THE UDAYA MOUNTAIN.

*FOREST OF REEDS

AGNI AND VAYU FLEW WITH THE SPARKS···

··· TO GANGA.

SHIVA HAS ASKED YOU TO CARRY THESE TO THE REED FOREST ON THE UDAYA MOUNTAIN.

AS SOON AS GANGA BROUGHT THEM INTO THE SHARAVANA···

···THE SPARKS TURNED INTO SIX BABIES!

AS PARVATI STEPPED CLOSER, THE BABIES MERGED INTO ONE.

MY SON!

HE IS MY SON. I HELD THE SPARKS.

NO, AGNI. HE IS MINE. I BROUGHT THEM TO THIS FOREST.

MY FOREST, O GANGA. HE WAS BORN IN MY FOREST OF REEDS. HE IS MY SON.

BUT WE ARE THE ONES WHO NURSED HIM, O GODDESS OF THE FOREST. HE IS OUR SON.

PEACE! PEACE! AS PARVATI'S SON HE WILL BE NAMED SKANDA AND AS THE SON OF THE GODDESS OF THE FOREST, SHARAVANA; AS THE KRITTIKAS' SON, KARTTIKEYA AND AS GANGA'S KUMARA; AS AGNI'S SON, MAHASENA AND AS MINE, GUHA.

HOW WILL I FONDLE A BABY WITH SIX HEADS?

THE NEXT MINUTE—

MY SON!

KARTTIKEYA WAS NOW LIKE ANY OTHER CHILD.

SOON, NINE DIVINE BEINGS EMERGED FROM THE LAKE.

THOSE ARE YOUR GANAS— VEERABAHU AND HIS COMPANIONS.

THEN, AFTER THE DEVAS HAD WORSHIPPED LORD KARTTIKEYA...

...SHIVA TOOK HIM TO HIS OWN ABODE, AT MOUNT KAILASA.

ONE DAY AT KAILASA—

PARVATI, THE TIME HAS COME FOR KARTTIKEYA TO SUBDUE TARAKASURA, SIMHAMUKHA, AND SURAPADMAN.

BUT HE IS JUST A CHILD, MY LORD, AND THEY ARE MIGHTY WARRIORS.

YES, BUT HE IS THE CHILD WITH THE DIVINE SPARK. BESIDES, HIS GANAS WILL GO WITH HIM.

SHIVA SUMMONED KARTTIKEYA AND VEERABAHU.

GET READY TO ATTACK SURAPADMAN AND HIS BROTHERS.

WHEN THE PREPARATIONS WERE COMPLETED—

YOU SHALL LEAD THE DEVAS TO VICTORY. CRUSH THE ASURAS AND LIBERATE THE DEVAS. HERE IS THE MATCHLESS VEL, YOUR SPEAR. MAY SUCCESS BE YOURS!

ARMED WITH THE SPEAR, KARTTIKEYA SET OUT IN PURSUIT OF THE ASURAS.

AFTER HE HAD COVERED SOME DISTANCE—

YOU WILL HAVE TO FACE ME, YOUNG BOY, BEFORE YOU PROCEED FURTHER.

IT WAS THE ASURA, KRAUNCHA IN THE FORM OF A MOUNTAIN.

WITHOUT A WORD, KARTTIKEYA HURLED HIS SPEAR···

···AND KRAUNCHA WAS NO MORE.

WHEN THE NEWS REACHED TARAKA—

KRAUNCHA DESTROYED? BY A SLIP OF A BOY?

WELL, WELL, LET ME GO AND SIZE HIM UP.

WHEN HE CAME FACE TO FACE WITH KARTTIKEYA—

DON'T MISUSE THE WEAPONS GRANTED TO YOU. RELEASE THE DEVAS. YOU AND YOUR BROTHERS WILL BE FORGIVEN.

HOW DARE YOU, YOU IMPUDENT BOY! GET AWAY...

...BEFORE I KILL YOU!

VICTORY TO SHIVA!

THIS WEAPON — THE WEAPON GIVEN TO ME BY SHIVA — CANNOT FAIL!

YOU HAVE EXHAUSTED ALL THOSE WEAPONS, TARAKA. NOW LET ME TRY THE ONE I HAVE.

KARTTIKEYA'S SPEAR FOUND ITS MARK.

TARAKASURA IS SLAIN!

VICTORY TO KARTTIKEYA!

LATER—

VEERABAHU, TARAKASURA'S DEATH MAY HAVE BROUGHT HIS BROTHERS TO THEIR SENSES. GO AS MY ENVOY TO SURAPADMAN AND ASK HIM TO STOP PERSECUTING THE DEVAS.

AS YOU COMMAND, MY LORD.

WHEN VEERABAHU REACHED SURAPADMAN'S CAPITAL, MAHENDRAPURI—

BEFORE I GO TO SURAPADMAN, I MUST SEE JAYANTA.

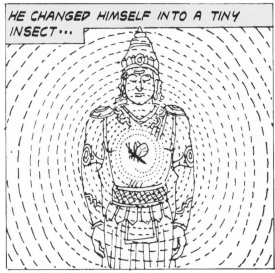

HE CHANGED HIMSELF INTO A TINY INSECT...

...AND FLEW INTO THE CITY.

IN THE PRISON—

JAYANTA, TARAKASURA IS DEAD. LORD KARTTIKEYA WILL SOON RESCUE YOU.

THEN HE FLEW INTO SURAPADMAN'S COURT.

I WILL ASSUME MY OWN FORM NOW. WILL SURAPADMAN OFFER ME A SEAT?

THE NEXT MOMENT—

A THRONE FOR ME! IT MUST BE THE WORK OF LORD KARTTIKEYA!

WHO... WHO ARE YOU?

I AM LORD KARTTIKEYA'S MESSENGER.

KARTTIKEYA! THE BOY WHO SLEW MY BROTHER!

YES, LORD KARTTIKEYA WANTS YOU TO RELEASE JAYANTA AND STOP TORTURING THE DEVAS OR ELSE...

...YOU WILL MEET WITH THE SAME FATE AS YOUR BROTHER!

A MERE CHILD DARES THREATEN ME! I'LL I'LL...

WHERE HAS HE GONE?

HE...HE'S VANISHED!

THERE WAS AN UNEASY SILENCE FOR A MOMENT. THEN SIMHAMUKHA SPOKE.

MY INSTINCT TELLS ME THAT THIS KARTTIKEYA IS NO ORDINARY BOY.

REMEMBER KRAUNCHA... TARAKA... WHY DON'T WE RELEASE...

SIMHAMUKHA!

COWARD! NOT ANOTHER WORD!

BROTHER, IT IS UNFORTUNATE THAT WISDOM IS OFTEN MISTAKEN FOR COWARDICE.

BY SPEAKING OUT, I HAVE DONE MY DUTY. NOW IT IS FOR YOU TO TAKE THE DECISION. I WILL GO BY IT.

IT'S WAR AGAINST THAT IMPUDENT BOY.

MEANWHILE VEERABAHU HAD REACHED KARTTIKEYA'S CAMP.

IT'S NO USE. SURAPADMAN WANTED TO CAPTURE ME TOO!

WELL, WE'LL MEET THEM IN BATTLE. PREPARE TO MARCH TO MAHENDRAPURI.

WHEN KARTTIKEYA'S ARMY REACHED THE OUTSKIRTS OF MAHENDRAPURI, SURAPADMAN SENT HIS SON BANUKOPAN TO SUBDUE THEM.

BANUKOPAN FELL UPON THE DEVA ARMY.

ON THE SECOND DAY OF THE BATTLE—

COME, BANUKOPAN. TODAY, YOU SHALL NOT RETURN HOME.

I CERTAINLY WON'T. NOT TILL I'VE KILLED EVERY ONE OF YOU.

VEERABAHU RUSHED AT HIM AND THE TWO FOUGHT LONG AND HARD.

AT LAST BANUKOPAN FELL AND THE ASURAS FLED IN PANIC.

THE DEATH OF BANUKOPAN SHOOK SURAPADMAN.

SAVE US, SIMHAMUKHA!

I WILL DO MY BEST, BROTHER.

SO THE NEXT DAY SIMHAMUKHA LED THE ATTACK. THE ARMY OF THE DEVAS REELED UNDER HIS ONSLAUGHT.

THEN SIMHAMUKHA SENT A MISSILE···

···WHICH WOUND ITSELF AROUND VEERABAHU, HIS BROTHER AND THE REST OF THE ARMY···

···AND HURLED THEM···

···FAR, FAR AWAY FROM THE BATTLEFIELD.

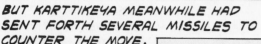

BUT KARTTIKEYA MEANWHILE HAD SENT FORTH SEVERAL MISSILES TO COUNTER THE MOVE.

SOON—

THEN KARTTIKEYA TURNED HIS ATTENTION TO SIMHAMUKHA.

YOU SHOULD NOT MISUSE THE POWERS ACQUIRED BY YOU. YOU SHOULD...

HAVE YOU COME HERE TO FIGHT OR TO PREACH?

AFTER A FIERCE BATTLE KARTTIKEYA HURLED INDRAYUDHA* AT SIMHAMUKHA.

AS SIMHAMUKHA FELL—

YOUR WEAPON HAS SHATTERED MY EGO. NOW I SEE YOU IN ALL YOUR GLORY. O LORD, BLESS ME.

THE MERCIFUL KARTTIKEYA BLESSED SIMHAMUKHA.

YOU SHALL SERVE GODDESS KALI AS HER VEHICLE.

*INDRA'S WEAPON, THE THUNDERBOLT

THE NEXT DAY SURAPADMAN HIMSELF LED THE ASURAS TO THE BATTLEFIELD.

WE MUST DEFEAT KARTTIKEYA! SHOW YOUR METTLE TODAY.

WHEN HE CAME FACE TO FACE WITH KARTTIKEYA—

MERCY OR DOOM? CHOOSE!

IMPUDENT CHILD! I HAVE COME TO SILENCE YOU ONCE AND FOR ALL.

THE TWO FOES MET.

THIS BOY IS NOT AS RAW AS I HAD EXPECTED! WHY, HE FIGHTS LIKE A SEASONED WARRIOR!

I'LL HAVE TO RESORT TO SORCERY. THAT'S THE ONLY WAY TO QUELL HIM!

THE NEXT MOMENT—

WH...WHAT IS THIS! MY CHARIOT IS MOVING TOWARDS THAT BOY.

SOON—

I MUST THANK YOU, SURAPADMAN, FOR PROVIDING ME WITH AN EXCELLENT CHARIOT.

I'LL CHANGE MY FORM AND ATTACK HIM.

SURAPADMAN QUICKLY ASSUMED THE FORM OF A HUGE BIRD ··

···AND CHARGED AT KARTTIKEYA.

KARTTIKEYA HOWEVER USING INDRA IN THE FORM OF PEACOCK AS HIS MOUNT···

BUT SURAPADMAN ESCAPED IN THE NICK OF TIME BY TAKING THE FORM OF A TREE.

···LASHED OUT AT HIM.

LEARN, O BLIND ONE! DARKNESS CANNOT HIDE BEFORE LIGHT!

AS THE SPEAR CUT THE TREE IN TWO, SURAPADMAN EMERGED UNSCATHED IN HIS NATURAL FORM.

I'LL CRUSH HIM WITH MY BULK!

SURAPADMAN CHARGED TOWARDS KARTTIKEYA.

I'LL CRUSH YOU UNDERFOOT. AND THAT WILL BE THE END OF YOU.

QUICK AS LIGHTNING, KARTTIKEYA HURLED HIS SPEAR AT HIM.

AND—

A·A·H

AS HE FELL, A GREAT CHANGE CAME OVER SURAPADMAN.

LORD, PARDON ME. I REPENT FOR MY EVIL ACTS. LORD, I SEEK REFUGE IN YOU.

KARTTIKEYA LOOKED AT THE FALLEN ASURA WITH COMPASSION.

SURAPADMAN, REPENTANCE WASHES AWAY ALL ONE'S SINS. YOU SHALL SERVE ME AS MY VEHICLE AND ALSO AS MY EMBLEM.

THUS SURAPADMAN ASSUMED TWO FORMS—ONE OF A PEACOCK TO SERVE AS A VEHICLE TO THE LORD AND ANOTHER OF A COCK TO ADORN KARTTIKEYA'S FLAG POST.

O KARTTIKEYA, WE BOW TO YOU IN REVERENCE.